The author had a rural upbringing in South Hanningfield, near Chelmsford in Essex, where his father was the village blacksmith. He left in 1944 to join the Royal Navy in which he served for five years. On leaving the Navy he became a Police Officer with the Metropolitan Police and lived for a short while in London before moving to Hertfordshire in 1957 where he has lived ever since.

He has always had a love of the countryside and an interest in old churches and other historic buildings and has spent much time travelling around the county looking at them and learning their history.

A
HERTFORDSHIRE
QUIZ

Walter Lodge

A
Hertfordshire
Quiz

Vanguard Press

VANGUARD PAPERBACK

© Copyright 2001
WALTER LODGE

A CIP catalogue record for this title is
available from the British Library
ISBN 1 903489 38 5

*Vanguard Press is an imprint of
Pegasus Elliot MacKenzie Publishers Ltd.*
www.pegasuspublishers.com

First Published in 2001

**Vanguard Press
Sheraton House Castle Park
Cambridge England**

Printed & Bound in Great Britain

FOREWORD

How often do we travel around the country and on our return wax lyrical about "other counties"?

Having lived in Hertfordshire nearly all my life and during that time travelled the length and breadth of the County, I firmly believed that there was little I didn't know about it.

Walter Lodge's book, a cocktail of quizzes and illustrations, compiled from his far reaching and detailed knowledge of Hertfordshire, has made me realise just how much I don't know.

Do not just attempt the quizzes - get out and visit the places and features mentioned and discover for yourself the heritage that is Hertfordshire's.

Jean Curl

Chairman - 1989 - 2001
Hertfordshire Federation of W.I.'s.

DEDICATION

To Betty, and to everybody who appreciates Hertfordshire, and all that it has to offer.

INTRODUCTION

For the purposes of this book I have taken Hertfordshire as it is today, that is post 1965, so that Barnet and district are not included and Potters Bar and district are.

To make the book more informative and interesting I have made many questions, and answers, much longer than they need have been simply for a quiz. The questions cover a wide range of subjects from Roman Hertfordshire to modern Town Twinning, from Castles to Village Public Houses and from Kings to Poachers.

Although in comparison with many counties Hertfordshire is small in area its proximity to London has ensured that it has a rich and interesting history, and many books have been written about it. It is from some of those books that I have gained much information for this Quiz Book. Many of the books refer to the same subjects, but often differ in detail, and in order not to perpetuate any inaccuracies, I have, where possible, visited all the places referred to in the book. Obviously many historical facts can no longer be verified by a visit and have to be accepted.

An example of how important it is to check information was born out during a visit to St. Albans Cathedral. I had intended to include a question about the impressive 15 feet long painting by Frank Salisbury, 'The Passing of Queen Eleanor,' but wanted to see it before I did so. I was unable to find it and on enquiry was told that it had been stolen some years before.

Often some of the older or more interesting buildings are, or were public houses, many with unusual or indeed unique names, such as The Chalkdrawers Arms, The Boys Home and The Rats Castle, and although many are closing or changing their names I thought they should be included. All those that are shown were still open at the time of going to print.

Seeking and checking the material has been very time consuming, but very interesting and educationally rewarding and has taken me to all parts of the county. I hope you the reader will get as much pleasure and interest from it as I have had in compiling it.

THE QUEEN'S HEAD PUBLIC HOUSE
AND ST. LEONARD'S CHURCH, SANDRIDGE.

CONTENTS

(Answers at back of book.)

QUIZ 1

ROMAN HERTFORDSHIRE

1. During the second Roman invasion of Britain in 54 B.C., the Roman armies were delayed in their advance by a major battle, probably near present day Wheathampstead, with the English and Belgic tribes. Who was the leader of the tribes?
2. Who was leading the Roman invasion at that time?
3. Verulamium was the chief Roman town in Hertfordshire. About which date did the Romans start to build it?
4. In A.D.61 who led the Iceni tribe from East Anglia to destroy the Roman settlements in the county?
5. What was the name of the Roman road leading out of London and passing through Verulamium (St. Albans) and Redbourn on its way to Chester?
6. Which Roman road lead out of Verulamium and passed through Tring on the way to Cirencester?
7. Which was the Roman road leading out of London and passing through Cheshunt, Ware and Royston on its way to Lincoln and York?

8. What was the name of the cross-country road, which came from Colchester and ran roughly along the route of the present A120 from Bishops Stortford to Puckeridge, and continued across the county to join the Icknield way near Baldock?

9. The second most important Roman town in the county was probably called Curcinati. It was at the intersection of two of the above roads. A Roman cemetery has been discovered there, but apart from that little excavation has been done. Which present village is close to it?

10. Where, recently, was a 3rd century Roman bathhouse discovered, and is now preserved in a steel vault?

QUIZ 2

KINGS AND QUEENS

1. Which king having stopped at Royston on his way to his coronation in London, liked it so much that he later had an inn turned into a Hunting Lodge and spent much time there?

2. Which king was first buried at Langley Priory after having been killed at Pontefract, and it was many years later before Henry V removed his remains to Westminster Abbey?

3. According to legend, which king while hawking near Wymondley, was nearly drowned when he fell off his horse into a stream? (There is a Public House sign at Little Wymondley depicting him being assisted out of the water.)

4. In which house in the east of the county did Mary and Elizabeth, daughters of Henry V111, live after the execution of Anne Boleyn? Later Mary set out from there to accept the throne.

5. Where did young Princess Elizabeth (Elizabeth I) live for ten years before being taken to imprisonment in the Tower of London?

6. Where was Elizabeth when she was told of the death of her sister Mary, and that she was now Queen?

7. Which king gave Hatfield House to Robert Cecil in exchange for Theobalds?

8. Which king did the Earl of Warwick capture at St. Albans during the first Battle of the Roses?

9. Which monarch was too nervous to travel by train over the viaduct at Digswell, and left the train and travelled by coach across the valley and rejoined the train at he other side?

10. Where in the county did H.R.H. Queen Elizabeth, the Queen mother spend much of her early childhood? (She is sometimes shown as being born there, but that is not so.)

QUIZ 3

GENERAL

1. We all know when and where Magna Carta was signed, but in which Hertfordshire town was it drafted?
2. What was the name of the former palace, to the North of Watford, where the first Duke of York, fifth son of Edward III was born?
3. In 1553, according to tradition, what significant event took place at Sopwell House, St. Albans?
4. In 1295, in which Hertfordshire town was The Model Parliament formed, to which every main town, city and borough in England sent two representatives?
5. In Ware, in 1553, what did the Marquis of Northampton do to cause him to be condemned to death and later pardoned?
6. Where in the County was James I when he died?
7. In the Domesday Survey of 1086 five boroughs were shown in Hertfordshire, which were they?
8. Hare Street House, Hare Street, near Buntingford is used as a summer retreat. By who?

9. The first tollgate in England was erected on a road in Hertfordshire in 1663, where was it?
10. Harry Andrews lived in George Lane, Royston, from 1776 to1820, and is buried in the churchyard there. He was a mathematician, astronomer and teacher. What is he remembered for?

QUIZ 4

CASTLES

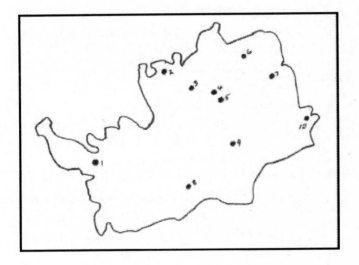

The diagram shows ten sites at which Norman castles were built. In some of them the motte, moat or bailey are still there, but in others there is no trace but they are well documented. Some may not have stood for very long, and indeed may not have been completed. Can you name them?

QUIZ 5

MORE CASTLES

1. In which castle did the Black Prince, son of Edward III, spend his honeymoon with his cousin Joan, the 'Fair Maid of Kent'?
2. In which castle did Queen Isabella, wife of Edward II, die, after having spent much of the latter part of her life there?
3. After his capture at Poitiers in 1356 in which castle was King John of France imprisoned after a short spell at Hertford castle?
4. Until 1225 only Berkhamsted and Hertford castles belonged to the King. Which castle did Henry III then acquire and place under the guardianship of the Archbishop of Canterbury?
5. In which town was Waytemore Castle, the 11th century stronghold of Bishop Maurice of London?
6. In which castle was David Bruce, King of Scotland, held captive for eleven years?
7. Of which castle was Geoffrey Chaucer Clerk of the Works in the early part of the 15th century; but it is not thought that he spent much time there?
8. Which Norman castle was built on the site of the former home of the Kings of Mercia?

9. In which castle did the English Church hold the first National Synod in 673?
10. Which castle is still owned by the Duchy of Cornwall?

QUIZ 6

AND MORE CASTLES

1. Which of the Hertfordshire castles did Thomas Becket build on a former stronghold site? He spent much time there.
2. Who was the last monarch to stay in Hertford Castle?
3. Which was the only Norman castle in the county to have a square keep?
4. Which castle did King John order to be destroyed in 1207 following a dispute with the church over the appointment of the Archbishop of Canterbury? The destruction was only partial, and the castle was later restored.
5. All Norman castles were in the form of a motte (raised mound) and bailey (enclosed area). Which of those in Hertfordshire had the highest motte?
6. Where, right in the north of the county, are there a clearly defined motte, and the remains of an exceptionally large moat, which is now protected as an Ancient Monument?
7. Which former castle, in the north east of the county, did Henry VIII give in turn to his first three wives?
8. In 1806 what was the gatehouse of Hertford Castle used for?

9. In the grounds of which castle were London statues stored for safekeeping during the Second World War.

10. On to which motte, the second highest in the county, did an American bomber crash during the Second World War?

5. REMAINS OF THE HIGHEST MOTTE
IN HERTFORDSHIRE.

10. NOW HEAVILY WOODED, THE REMAINS OF
THE SECOND HIGHEST MOTTE IN THE COUNTY.

QUIZ 7

HUNDREDS

In Saxon England counties were divided into administrative divisions known as Hundreds, because there were about 100 households in each division.
The map below shows the eight Hundreds into which Hertfordshire was divided. Can you name them? You will see that three of them are fragmented.

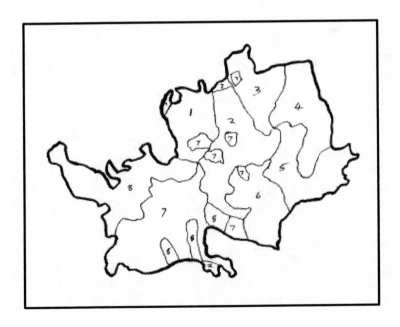

QUIZ 8

ST. ALBANS CATHEDRAL

1. The cathedral stands on the supposed site where St. Alban was martyred in 209 A.D. It has replaced a monastery that was built there in 793. Who built the monastery?
2. The first Norman Abbot of St. Albans, Paul de Caen, replaced the Saxon monastery with an abbey, which now forms much of the present cathedral. In which year was the abbey completed?
3. Which unique 15th century wooden structure with its rich traceried panels and quaint carvings, dominates the north side of the Saint's Chapel?
4. Who, in the late 19th century, was the wealthy benefactor responsible for much restoration throughout the cathedral and in particular the restoration of the west front?
5. What is depicted in a large painting on wood in the south aisle?
6. Whose chantry chapel is behind an elaborate, possibly 13th century, iron grille in the south aisle?
7. On the floor of the Wheathampstead chantry is an exceptionally fine brass, believed by a Flemish craftsman. Who is depicted in it?

8. Who was the architect in charge of repairs to save the central tower from collapsing, and other restoration work, from 1856-1877?

9. Who opened the new Chapter House on 8th July 1982?

10. On 26th September 1989, H.R.H the Princess of Wales unveiled a window in the north transept. What does it commemorate?

QUIZ 9

MORE ST. ALBANS CATHEDRAL

1. It was well into the 19th century that St. Albans became a cathedral. Prior to that it was the abbey church. What date was the first Bishop enthroned?
2. An effigy of the first Bishop lies on his tomb in the north transept, who was he?
3. Which four figures are depicted in golden robes on the ornate cover of the marble font?
4. The magnificent stone screen built in about 1484, and regarded as one of the finest in England, was badly damaged during the Dissolution and remained in that condition until it was repaired during the 19th century. Who was the benefactor responsible for the repairs?
5. Approximately how many statues are there on the screen?
6. At the bottom of the screen there is a sculptured panel depicting Jesus rising from the tomb. Who was the famous sculptor?
7. What is displayed on the oak lectern in the retro-choir, under a golden St. George and the Dragon?

8. The Bishop's throne is modern, but rich in beautiful carvings. Who is depicted at the top in front of the canopy?

9. Hanging in the chapel of the Lady of the Four Tapers is a monogrammed tapestry of the organisation responsible for restoring the chapel in 1931. What was the organisation?

10. Richard of Wallington was Abbot from 1327 to 1336. As well as being a theologian he was a mathematician and astronomer. He is best remembered for an invention which took up much of his time, but which was destroyed during the Dissolution. It was later found well documented in the Bodleian Library at Oxford and a replica was built and is now working in the cathedral. What is it?

QUIZ 10

HOUSES

1. The Salisbury family have been prominent in British politics for many years. Which is their stately home?

2. Which house in the west of the county was the family home of the Earls of Essex?

3. Which house was built by Sir Robert Lytton, Keeper of the Wardrobe to King Henry VII, in the late 15th century, and is still occupied by the Lytton family?

4. Sir Francis Bacon, Lord Chancellor to James I, philosopher and noted essayist, lived in which great house in St. Albans?

5. Which house, in the west of the county, was given to the Earl of Oxford as a reward for his services at Bosworth Field, and later became the home of the Duke of Monmouth?

6. What is the name of the magnificent house, set in beautiful gardens, at Little Gaddesden, the former home of the Duke of Bridgewater, the canal pioneer?

7. Which house, in the east of the county, which had been prominent in the social life of the county, was bought by the Duke of Wellington sometime after the Battle of

Waterloo, but it is thought that he never lived in it?

8. Which house, near Lemsford, was the home of two noted Victorian Prime Ministers, Lord Melbourne and Lord Palmerston?

9. Which house, in the east of the county, was in 1683 the scene of an unsuccessful plot to assassinate Charles II and his brother the future James II?

10. Which large house, near what is now Welwyn Garden City, was the family home of the Cowper family. The first earl, a former Lord High Chancellor was buried there?

QUIZ 11

HATFIELD HOUSE

1. Who, until the early 16th century owned the site on which Hatfield House now stands?
2. Who, during the 15th century began to build Hatfield Palace on this site?
3. After the death of Queen Elizabeth I, who had the present house built?
4. How long did it take to complete, and what date is built into the stonework on the south porch?
5. What shape was the house when it was first completed?
6. Two famous paintings hang in the hall, the 'Rainbow Portrait' and the 'Ermine Portrait.' Who is portrayed in them?
7. The Dowager First Marchioness of Salisbury, a keen horsewoman, was in 1793 the first woman to become Master of Foxhounds. Her riding became quite legendary but had nothing to do with her unfortunate death in 1835. How did she die?
8. Of which Marquis of Salisbury is there a large statue in front of the main gates of the house?
9. Who was the sculptor?
10. To what use was the house put during the Second World War?

8. STATUE IN FRONT OF HATFIELD HOUSE.

QUIZ 12

DISTRICT COUNCILS

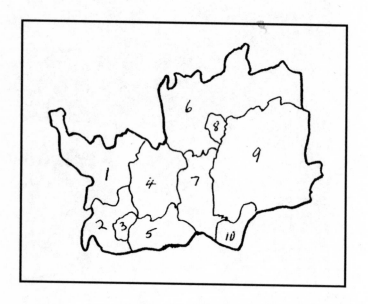

There are 10 District Councils within the County.
How many can you name?

Quiz 13

CHURCHES AND OTHER RELIGIOUS BUILDINGS

1. Which is the largest parish church in the county, and the only one to have a charnel house, that is a cellar or crypt where bones removed from graves are kept? It also has a sundial on the tower, with the inscription 'In Thanksgiving for the restoration of Charles II'?

2. The oldest purpose-built Friends Meeting House (Quakers) in the world that is still in use is in Hertfordshire. Where is it?

3. What type of religious building is there in Cambridge Road, Watford and The Causeway, Bishops Stortford?

4. What type of religious buildings are to be found in Oswald Road, St. Albans, Nascot Road, Watford, Watling Street, Radlett and Croxdale Road, Boreham Wood?

5. John Francis Bentley is remembered as the architect who designed Westminster Cathedral. Prior to that which Roman Catholic Church in Hertfordshire, did he design, which is regarded as a 'Bentley Gem'?

6. Apart from St. Albans Cathedral, which is the oldest complete Norman church in the county?

(It has a porch, which was added in the 18th century).

7. Where is the only parish church in the county dedicated to St. Vincent?

8. Where is there a brick and flint chapel, which was built in 1612 by Sir James Altham, on an 8th century monastic site? Inside are effigies of Sir James in his judge's robes and his wife.

9. In which town is the tall, 500 years old, hilltop church of St. Michael, with its peal of ten bells? It is one of the few in the county to have misericords (brackets to rest on whilst standing) and these are said to have come from old St. Pauls. Francis Rhodes, father of Cecil Rhodes was a vicar here.

10. Completed in 1963, in which town is the unusual redbrick Roman Catholic church of St. Teresa of the Child Jesus, with two tall towers with hipped roofs?

1. THE LARGEST PARISH CHURCH IN
HERTFORDSHIRE.

6. THE OLDEST COMPLETE
NORMAN CHURCH IN THE COUNTY.

7. ST. VINCENT.

QUIZ 14

FAMOUS PEOPLE

1. Which Bavarian born artist settled in Bushey in the 1870's where he founded a famed art school? He also wrote music and was a pioneer of early films. His paintings include 'Back to Life' and 'The Last Muster,' a colourful picture of Chelsea Pensioners. He died in 1914.

2. Which great agriculturist, who lived at Harpenden until his death in 1900, started the Rothamsted Experimental Agricultural Station; the first of its type in the world? He also pioneered artificial fertilisers.

3. Which famous poet was born in Berkhamsted in 1731, where his father was Rector? John Gilpin is one of his best-known poems.

4. Who was Ware's 18th century Quaker Poet? He is best remembered locally for his shell-lined folly in the road named after him.

5. Which famous sculptor lived and worked at Hogsland, Perry Green near Much Hadham, until his death in 1986?

6. Which artist and illustrator lived all her life at Wildings, a house near Welwyn, until her death in 1990, aged 84? She is best known for

her illustrations in many Enid Blyton books including all the original Famous Five series.

7. Which famous Victorian actress, after whose son Gordon Craig, the theatre in Stevenage is named lived, for many years in Harpenden?

8. Until his untimely death in 1984, which much-loved comedian lived in Harpenden?

9. Who was the pioneer of garden cities? Letchworth was the first one planned and built in 1903, followed by Welwyn Garden City in 1920.

10. Which Quaker physician, born in Bishops Stortford, was noted for his work in connection with inoculation against smallpox? He went to Russia at the invitation of the Empress to inoculate her and her son, and was rewarded by being made a Baron, as well as a financial reward. He was Member of Parliament for Hertford and a local benefactor. There was a public house named after him in Hertford, and he is buried in the Quaker Burial Ground in Bishops Stortford.

QUIZ 15

PUBLIC HOUSES 1

There are a wide variety of Public House names throughout the county, many of them unusual or unique. Which towns are the following groups in?

1. Edward The Confessor; The Man in the Moon Corey's Mill; Our Mutual Friend
2. The Rats Castle; The Ancient Britain; The Fighting Cocks; The King Harry;
3. The Fishery Inn; The Golden Cockerel; The Steamcoach; Ye Olde Projectionist
4. The Leviathian; The Load of Hay; The Wag and Bone; The Wishing Well
5. The Jockey; The Chequers; The North Star; The Old Bull;
6. The Old Pond; The Old English Gentleman; The Old Anchor; The Roman Urn
7. The Half Moon; The Black Lion; The George; The Boars Head
8. The Red Hart; The Angels Reply; The Tut and Shive; The George
9. The Duncombe Arms; The Sportsman; The Dolphin; The Old Barge
10. The Saracen's Head; The Old Punch Rouse; The Rifle Volunteer; The Bulls Head

1. THE MAN IN THE MOON.

2. THE RATS CASTLE.

5. THE JOCKEY.

7. THE BOARS HEAD.

9. THE OLD BARGE.

QUIZ 16

RAILWAYS

1. In 1838 the first railway line through the county was completed. Which line was it?
2. Which major work was carried out in the county in order that the line complied with the prescribed gradient regulations?
3. The second main line ran north through the Lea Valley but was restricted by finance and was completed in stages. In 1840 it reached Broxbourne. Where had it reached in 1842?
4. In 1863 a branch line was completed from St. Margarets. Where did it run to until closed by Dr. Beeching in 1963?
5. Which loop line, which closed in 1909, was reopened in 1960, and is still in use today?
6. After the usual trouble with landowners the Great Northern Railway was completed from London to Peterborough in 1850, via the outstanding Digswell Viaduct where it crosses the Mimram Valley. Who designed the viaduct?
7. Who was the contractor in charge of the construction of the viaduct?
8. How high is the viaduct above the valley bottom, and how many arches are there in it?

9. Also in 1850 the first branch line from this line ran from Hitchin. Where did it terminate?
10. Until 1952 to which town in the Southwest of the county did a through line run from St. Albans?

4. THE FORMER BOOKING HALL AT BRAUGHING
STATION, ON THE BRANCH LINE THAT RAN FROM
ST. MARGARET'S. (IT IS NOW A PRIVATE HOUSE).

6. THE DIGSWELL VIADUCT BUILT
FOR THE GREAT NORTHERN RAILWAY.

QUIZ 17

GENERAL

1. What is the name of the pre-roman track, following the Chiltern ridge from Bedfordshire across the north of the county to Royston and beyond?
2. What is the name of the Iron Age hill fort on the heavily wooded steep hillside above Hexton?
3. Parts 0f ancient earthworks are still traceable on Berkhamsted Common. By which name are they known?
4. What is the name of the large earthworks to the east of Wheathampstead, believed to be the site where the Catuvellauni fought a prolonged battle with the Romans, and held up their advance to St. Albans during the second invasion of Britain in 54 B.C.?
5. What is the name of the former Iron Age earthworks near Ashwell. There is very little to see there nowadays, but outlines can be seen from the air?
6. Site of a similar hill fort on the edge of what is now Letchworth?
7. What unique feature did workmen digging in the Butter Market discover in Royston in

1742. It is now open to the Public on certain days or by appointment?

8. Where was the home of the wealthy, and rather eccentric barrister and benefactor of St. Albans Abbey, Lord Grimthorpe?

9. Which 16th century churchman and statesman owned at least three large houses in Hertfordshire, Cheshunt Great House, Moor Park, Rickmansworth, and Delamere House, Great Wymondely?

10. Where in the county is a recently restored 17th century Post Mill that had been working until 1930?

4. REMAINS OF EARTHWORKS TO
THE EAST OF WHEATHAMSTEAD.

THIS ENTRENCHMENT
IS PART OF A
BRITISH CITY
BUILT IN THE
I CENTURY B.C.
IT WAS PROBABLY HERE THAT
JULIUS CAESAR
DEFEATED THE BRITISH KING
CASSIVELLAUNUS
IN 54 B.C.

4. PLAQUE BY EARTHWORKS.

10. RESTORED 17TH CENTURY POST MILL.

QUIZ 18

INDUSTRIES – PAST AND PRESENT

1. In 1488 John Tate had a mill in Hertford and became the first person in England to produce a certain product. There is some suggestion that the mill may have been on the site of Sele Mill, which was recently demolished to make way for houses. A chimney was left standing as a monument. What did John Tate produce?

2. What did Edward Perks start to grow near Hitchin in 1823? He regularly grew about 35 acres, and with his partner Llewellyn distilled the crop into a best selling product; others later carried on the business into the 20th century but sales declined and it ceased in the late 1950's.

3. During the 18th century what did John Briant make at his foundry in Hertford?

4. During most of the 18th century, and the early part of the 19th, which mill on the river Rib made fine paper used in the production of bibles? By the middle of the 19th century it had become a sawmill, and it is now a private house.

5. Which industry, which used to be carried on in many places in the county, such as West

Hyde and Flamstead, is still thriving at Whitwell?

6. For which product was Rochford's of Turnford well known?

7. Caleb Hitch was buried in Ware churchyard in1851, and his occupation is shown on his tombstone. Many examples of his products can be seen in the Ware and Hertford areas. What did he make?

8. What type of industry did Lanes at Potten End carry on in the early part of the 20th century? Their name is perpetuated by at least one of their well-known products.

9. Which type of industry was carried on by G.Webb and Company at Horns Mill, Hertford, and W.G. Russell and Sons at Hitchin?

10. Between 1922 and the Second World War, when they turned to tank repairing and producing munitions, what was the main product of D. Wickham and Company of Ware, which they exported world wide?

QUIZ 19

*PEOPLE – FAMOUS, NOTEWORTHY
OR INFAMOUS*

1. Which favourite of Edward II, on whom he had bestowed the Honour of Berkhamsted, was executed at Warwick in 1312, and buried in Kings Langley?
2. By which name was Caroline Ponsonby, wife of Lord Melbourne of Brocket Hall, better known?
3. Which great poet was she madly in love with, and surprised and shocked in 1824, many years after he had tired of her, to be told that a funeral cortege passing the estate, just as she was driving out of it, was his?
4. During the 17th century which 'friend' of royalty lived in a house adjacent to Salisbury Hall, near London Colney. The son she gave birth to there become the Duke of St. Albans?
5. In the mid 17th century the lady of the manor at Markyate was Kathleen Ferrers. For what exploits is she remembered?
6. Wrotham Park, in the south of the county near Bentley Heath, was built in 1754, but its unfortunate owner did not live long to enjoy it, as he was shot three years later for neglect of duty. Who was he?

7. Jane Welham, a washerwoman from Walkern, was tried at Hertford Assizes in 1712, found guilty and sentenced to death. She was later reprieved, and was the last person in England to be sentenced to death for that offence. What was the offence?

8. Who was the Magistrate who had committed her for trial, and who later became a judge? He is best remembered for his detailed writings in his History of Hertfordshire?

9. Another famous antiquarian and Hertfordshire Historian lived at Hinxworth Place and is buried in St. Mary's churchyard in Watford. Who?

10. During the 17th century Elizabeth Greenhall lived in Abbots Langley. She is now in the Guinness Book of Records. Why?

QUIZ 20

PUBLIC HOUSES 2

In which towns are the following groups of Public Houses?

1. The Hen and Chickens; The Engine; The Old White Horse; The George
2. The Silver Cup; The Fox; The Marquis of Granby; The Plough and Harrow
3. The White Swan; The Salisbury Arms; The Bull; The Golden Lion
4. The New Mill House; The Robin Hood; The Rose and Crown; The Bell
5. The Strafford Arms; The Potters; The Cask and Stillage; The Lion
6. The Lamb; The Goat; The Boat; The King's Head
7. The Good Intent; The Gate; The King William IV; The Three Horseshoes
8. The Chieftain; The Hollybush; The Fountain; The Cork and Cask
9. The Black Bull; The Jolly Sailors; The Chequers; The Railway
10. The Comet; The Wrestlers; The Red Lion; The Cavendish Arms

1. THE HEN AND CHICKENS.

4. THE ROBIN HOOD.

7. THE KING WILLIAM IV.

8. THE CHIEFTAIN.

10. THE SIGN OF THE COMET HOTEL.

QUIZ 21

MONUMENTS AND MEMORIALS

1. At Coleman Green, north east of St. Albans, all that remains of a cottage is a chimney, which is now kept as a memorial to someone who is said to have preached in, and possibly lodged in the cottage. Who was he?

2. At Cuffley there is a memorial to Captain William Leefe Robinson V.C. of the Royal Flying Corps. Which exploit does it commemorate?

3. On the Ashridge Estate to the west of Berkhamsted, is an imposing granite Doric column, surmounted by an urn, which was erected in 1832. Who does it commemorate?

4. Between Wadesmill and High Cross, north of Ware, there is an obelisk with an inscription that states that 'On the spot where stands this monument in the month of June 1785, Thomas Clarkson resolved to devote his life to ----'. What did he resolve to devote his life to?

5. Which two royal occasions are commemorated by a tall obelisk on Therfield Heath beside the Royston to Baldock road?

6. Near Willian, east of Hitchin, is a memorial to Captain Hamilton and Lieutenant Wyness-

Stuart to commemorate which event on 6th September 1912?

7. In a field at Standon Green End, close to High Cross, there is a stone memorial surrounded by railings. It commemorates which achievement by Vincento Lunardi on 15th September 1784?

8. The Eleanor Cross, at Waltham Cross, is a well-known landmark. Which king had it erected and why?

9. At Great Amwell, near Ware, there is a memorial to Sir Hugh Middleton. What does it commemorate?

10. Where in the county is there a large memorial to the American 398th Bombardment Group (Heavy), to commemorate the 195 daylight bombing missions which were made from there by B17 (Flying Fortress) Bombers between 6th May, 1944 and 25th April, 1945, during which time 58 planes failed to return?

1. CHIMNEY AT COLEMAN GREEN.

2. MEMORIAL AT CUFFLEY.

6. MEMORIAL NEAR WILLIAN.

7. LUNARDI'S MONUMENT AT
STANDON GREEN END.

QUIZ 22

MORE HOUSES

1. What was the name of Lord Burghley's magnificent palace built in Cheshunt about 1564?

2. Which house in the west of the county was the home of Sir William Gore, first Director of the Bank of England, and later home to the Rothschild family?

3. Which house in St. Albans, which was demolished in 1837, was the home of the Duke of Marlborough before Blenheim was built?

4. On the northern outskirts of Watford what was the name of the house built in 1756 for the Earl of Clarendon?

5. Which large house in Hertford, built in Tudor style with a long range of gables and mullioned windows was formerly the home of the banking family the Abel-Smiths; then a Dr. Barnardo's home, and until recently was occupied by Hertfordshire County Council?

6. Which house, to the north of Potters Bar, was built in 1599 by Sir Ralph Coningsby and later became the home of Charles II's minister the Earl of Danby, who later became the Duke of Leeds?

7. Where, for nearly 1000 years, was the country home of the Bishops of London?

8. Which large Georgian mansion near Hunton Bridge, was the home of Robert Raymond a former Lord Chief Justice?

9. What was the name of the former mansion near London Colney that was the home of Sir Thomas Pope, the founder of Trinity College, Oxford?

10. Cromwell executed Arthur, Lord Capel because he supported Charles I, and his son later died in the Tower of London for his part in a plot to kill Charles II. Which house in the east of the county was their family home?

QUIZ 23

GENERAL

1. Christ's Hospital School for girls (Blue Coat School) was well known in Hertford until it closed in 1988, when the girls went to join the boys, who had long since moved to Horsham in Surrey. The original school was not in Hertford, but was moved there in 1760 from another town in the county, which still has a statue of a blue-coated boy standing over the entrance to what was the old school. Where is it?

2. In which Hertfordshire village, the only one in England to have them, are there engraved stone plaques on the front of the houses from which men went to fight in the First World War and failed to return?

3. When and where did the last public execution take place in Hertfordshire?

4. The gallows on which that execution took place have been preserved. Where are they now?

5. The only prison now in Hertfordshire is a modern one at Bovingdon. Where was the last old one and when did it close?

6. Which village has an unusual concrete, beehive shaped lock-up, with the words 'BE

SOBER - BE VIGILANT' and 'DO WELL - FEAR NOUGHT' engraved into it?

7. In which village is there a square, sturdy looking, wooden, 17th century lock-up, close to an inn of the same period with a gantry crossing the road, with a fox being pursued by hounds on it?

8. Which famous plot was discovered as a result of a letter being delivered to Lord Mounteagle at Furneux Pelham Hall, telling him not to attend Parliament?

9. Where, in the county, is a large statue of Saint Joan of Arc, which was unveiled by the French Ambassador in 1939?

10. In which town centre is there a modern statue of a mother with a child on her back, entitled 'Joyride'?

1. STATUE OF BLUE-COATED BOY.

6. BEEHIVE SHAPED LOCK-UP.

7. STURDY WOODEN LOCK-UP.

9. STATUE OF JOAN OF ARC.

QUIZ 24

NOTEWORTHY HERTFORDIANS

1. Which colonial post did Robert, First Earl of Lytton, of Knebworth, hold from 1876 to 1880?

2. Lady Constance Lytton, who died in 1923, was a leader in which movement early this century?

3. Until it was pulled down in 1836, Gobions was a large mansion near Brookmans Park. Whose family home was it until his execution in 1535?

4. Who was born at Ware Park in 1608 and became a leading Royalist and close associate of Prince Charles (Charles II). He was captured at the Battle of Worcester, but later released. His last appointment was as Ambassador to Spain, where he died in 1666?

5. Which former owner of Standon Lordship was a leading statesman for nearly fifty years during the reigns of Henry VIII and Elizabeth? He was particularly involved in Scottish affairs, and had many dealings with Mary, Queen of Scots. His tomb and effigy are in Standon Parish Church.

6. Which industrialist, after who a process for smelting iron is named, was born in 1813 at Charlton House, just to the South of Hitchin?

7. Nicholas Breakspear was born in Abbots Langley about 800 years ago. His family was poor and his father became a monk at St. Albans. Which unique position did he acquire in 1154?

8. Whose family home was Blakesware, near Widford (The house where Charles Lamb spent much of his childhood whilst visiting his grandmother who was housekeeper there)? He was the Member of Parliament for Lewes from 1763 to 1768; for Hertfordshire from 1768 to 1807 and for Higham Ferrers from 1812 until his death in 1822. He was a strong supporter of the abolition of slavery movement?

9. Tring is well known for its Natural History museum. Many of the specimens in it had been in a private collection, which was bequeathed to the British Museum. By whom?

10. Which retired Governor General of South Africa, son of a former Prime Minister, lived in Dane End House, near Ware, from 1918 to 1930?

QUIZ 25

VILLAGE PUBLIC HOUSES

Many village Public Houses have unusual and interesting names; some of them are unique.
Ten are listed below but they are not opposite their correct village. Can you pair them up correctly?

1. The Fisherman's Tackle
2. The Old Guinea
3. The Half Moon
4. The Three Hammers
5. The Boys Home
6. The Long and Short Arm
7. The Pear and Partridge
8. The Jolly Waggoner
9. The Round Bush
10. The Sword in Hand

A. Abbots Langley
B. Chiswell Green
C. London Colney
D. Ridge
E. Aldenham
F. Westmill
G. Lemsford
H. West Hyde
I. Wilstone
J. Ardeley

2. THE OLD GUINEA.

5. THE BOYS HOME.

6. THE LONG AND SHORT ARM.

7. THE PEAR AND PARTRIDGE.

QUIZ 26

CHURCHES AND CHURCHYARDS

1. The only Royal tomb in the county is that of the first Duke of York, Edmund, fifth son of Edward III. In which parish church is it?
2. In which church was the author George Orwell (Eric Blair) married in 1936. A copy of his marriage certificate is displayed in the church?
3. In which parish did Thomas Becket have his first living as a rector?
4. Most Hertfordshire churches have a square tower and a small steeple known as a 'Hertfordshire Spike.' Which is the only church in the County where the tower has a gabled saddleback roof?
5. Where is All Saints, a modern church with a hexagonal interior? The first purpose built church to be shared by Anglicans. Roman Catholics and Methodists.
6. Lieutenant Colonel Arthur Martin-Leake was awarded a Victoria Cross for outstanding bravery during the Boer War, and a second Victoria Cross for another act of outstanding bravery during the First World War. He is the only double holder of the Victoria Cross to be

buried in Britain. In which churchyard is he buried?

7. In which churchyard is the grave of Thomas Pickford, the founder of the haulage and removal firm?

8. In which village is the 'lock-up' built as part of the lych-gate leading into the churchyard?

9. In the county we have one of only two churches in England dedicated to a 3rd century bishop and theologian. The parish also takes its name from him. Which church and parish?

10. In which parish church is there a brass plaque, and outside a gravestone commemorating the life of Peter the Wild Boy? The boy had been living like an animal in a forest near Hanover, and walking on his hands and feet. King George I brought him to England; and attempts were made to educate him but he was incapable of learning, and never learned to speak. He died in 1785 at about 72 years of age?

4. TOWER WITH A GABLED SADDLEBACK ROOF.

6. THE MARTIN-LEAKE GRAVES.

8. LYCH GATE WITH LOCK-UP.

10. GRAVE OF PETER THE WILD BOY.

QUIZ 27

GENERAL

1. Where, in Hertfordshire, was King James Ist when he signed the Death Warrant for Sir Walter Raleigh?

2. Where is the only long barrow in the county, together with Bronze Age and Neolithic burial mounds?

3. In which large red-bricked house near Essendon did Samuel Whitbread, the brewer, live from 1765 until his death thirty years later?

4. The Women's Institute, (now W.I.) was first formed in 1879 in Stoney Creek, Ontario, Canada by Adelaide Hoodless. The first group in England or Wales was in 1915. Which was the first group in Hertfordshire, and when was it formed?

5. On 13th October 1915, right at the start of German air raids on England during the First World War, high explosive and incendiary bombs were dropped on which Hertfordshire town, causing much damage and several deaths?

6. Although there are many stories, in many places, about Dick Turpin, it does seem that he did spend some time hiding in a public

house now in Stevenage using the name Palmer, his mother's maiden name, shortly before his ride to York. Which public house was it?

7. Which 17th century diarist, who lodged at what is now The Crown and Falcon public house in Puckeridge, wrote of the bad condition of the road there?

8. Which is the only Hertfordshire football club in the Football League or Premier Division?

9. What is the name of their home ground?

10. Rickmansworth, Chorleywood, Croxley and Watford are the only stations in Hertfordshire, which are on the London Underground system. Which line are they on?

6. PUBLIC HOUSE ASSOCIATED
WITH DICK TURPIN.

7. THE CROWN AND FALCON AT PUCKERIDGE.

QUIZ 28

AUTHORS

1. Which Victorian author, poet and friend of Charles Dickens lived at Knebworth House? His books include Rienzi and the Last Days of Pompeii.

2. Which famous author lived at which had originally been the rectory at Ayot St. Lawrence, until his death in 1950?

3. Which author, poet and essayist once owned Button Snap, a picturesque thatched cottage at Cherry Green, near Westmill? There is a large marble plaque with a relief carving of his head, on the bank outside the cottage.

4. Which 19th century author lived for many years at Waltham House, in Waltham Cross?

5. Which author, who died in 1970, spent his boyhood at 'Rooks Nest' near Stevenage? He is best known for his novel Howard's End, which is based on Rooks Nest.

6. Which famous authoress spent much of her young adulthood at Quinbury, a rather remote farmhouse near Braughing?

7. Which author, who died in 1991, was a pupil at Berkhamsted School, where his father was headmaster?

8. Which author of a famous series of boy's books lived in Cowbridge, Hertford, until his death in 1968?

9. Which famous children's author used to spend much time with her grandparent's at Camfield Place, near Essendon? She is thought to have based one of her best- known stories on the garden there.

10. Which prolific romantic novelist lived at Camfield Place until her death in May 2000 at the age of 98?

3. BUTTON SNAP.

3. PLAQUE ON GRASS VERGE
OUTSIDE BUTTON SNAP.

QUIZ 29

RIVERS

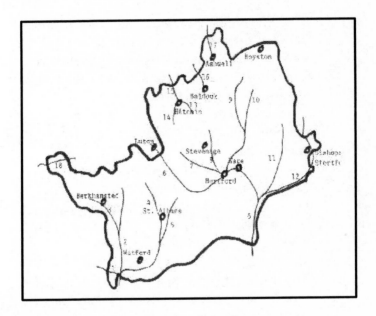

The map shows eighteen rivers that run through the county, the New River is not included.
How many can you name?

QUIZ 30

HERTFORDSHIRE IN LITERATURE

1. The following are extracts from conversations between three gentlemen on foot, 1st Gent: "I have stretched my legs to overtake you, hoping your business may occasion you towards Ware, whither I am going."
   2nd Gent: "For my purpose is to drink my morning's draught at the Thatched House in Hoddesdon."
   3rd Gent: "I shall by your favour bear you company as far as Theobald's."
   From which book, and by whom?

2. In a sonnet, 'The Lord of Light Shakes Off,' who wrote the following lines? "Slow journeying on
   To the green plains of pleasant Hertfordshire."

3. From which poem, and by whom, do the following lines come?
   Said John - "It is my wedding day,
   And all the world would stare,
   If wife should dine at Edmonton
   And I should dine at Ware."

4. Which Elizabethan house near Tewin forms the title of a novel started by Joseph Strutt and completed by Sir Walter Scott?

5. In which of Shakespeare's plays does the following line occur?
"Although the sheet were big enough for the bed of Ware in England."

6. Which English poet refers to walking, "The Roman road to Wendover by Tring and Lilley Hoo"?

7. In which novel, and by who is Mr. Darcy - 'not at all liked in Hertfordshire'?

8. 'The slow drive home by motor-car,
A heavy Rover Landaulette,
Through Welwyn, Hatfield, Potters Bar,
Tweed and cigar smoke, gloom and wet.'
From a poem entitled 'Hertfordshire,' by which poet?

9. 'For Cambridge people rarely smile,
Being urban, squat, and packed with guile;
And Royston men in the far South
Are black and fierce and strange of mouth;'
From a poem entitled 'The Old Vicarage, Grantchester', by which poet?

10. Who wrote:
There was an old person of Ware,
Who rode on the back of a bear:
When they asked, - 'Does it trot?'
He said: 'Certainly not.
He's a Moppsikon Floppsikon bear.'

QUIZ 31

NATURAL HISTORY

1. Herons nest regularly in the county, but nowhere in large numbers. The number of nests in the heronries varies from year to year, but which heronry has consistently had the most nests since the birds first nested there in 1957?
2. What is most unusual about this heronry?
3. For what reason have the springs at Ashwell been designated a Site of Special Scientific Interest?
4. Which bird, a common resident in Northern Scotland and Ireland, is now a very rare occasional visitor to the county during spring and autumn when some birds from the most northerly part of its range {Scandinavia) are migrating or returning to breed. It used to be a common winter visitor, especially to the downs in the Royston area, where it became the symbol of the local newspaper?
5. Where is the tree still growing that the 18th century naturalist Gilbert White described as 'probably the finest and most stately oak now growing in the South East of England'?

6. After an absence as a breeding bird for sixty years, which bird successfully nested on Hillfield Park Reservoir in 1990?

7. Which tree, common in Hertfordshire, Essex and parts of southeast England, but uncommon elsewhere, used to be used extensively for fuel to roast barley in the numerous maltings throughout the county?

8. Which is the only place in the county where the Fat Dormouse or Edible Dormouse - *Glis glis* - lives in the wild?

9. Which member of the plover family, now a very rare spring visitor to the county while returning from migration to its northern breeding grounds, used to be a regular spring visitor to the high ground in the Royston area? Special days out used to be held by so-called 'sportsmen' to shoot them as they arrived and attempted to rest and feed before moving on?

10. Which large bird used to be hunted by falconers, including King James I on Therfield Heath, but was last seen in the county at the beginning of the 18th century shortly before it became extinct in Britain? Recent attempts have been made to reintroduce it on Salisbury Plain.

QUIZ 32

MORE VILLAGE PUBLIC HOUSES

See quiz 25

1.	The Dog and Partridge	**A.**	Pirton
2.	The Rest and Welcome	**B.**	Rushden
3.	The Cabinet	**C.**	Heronsgate
4.	The Motte and Bailey	**D.**	Haultwick (Pronounced Artic)
5.	The Bell and Shears	**E.**	Eastwick
6.	The Dumb Bell	**F.**	Abbots Langley
7.	The Moon and Stars	**G.**	Reed
8.	The Land of Liberty Peace and Plenty	**H.**	Maple Cross
9.	The Dusty Miller	**I.**	Nomansland, Wheathampstead
10.	The Wicked Lady	**J.**	Redbourn

4. THE MOTTE AND BAILEY.

8. THE LAND OF LIBERTY,
PEACE AND PLENTY.

9. THE DUSTY MILLER.

10. THE WICKED LADY.

QUIZ 33

TOWN TWINNING

Many Hertfordshire towns are twinned with towns on the continent. Some are twinned with two or three in different countries. Most of the towns that are twinned have the name of the twin town shown on the town name signs on roads leading into the town.

Hertfordshire towns are listed below, with a list of twin towns on the right, but they are not twinned correctly. Can you sort them out?

1.	Potters Bar	**A.** Nanterre, France
2.	Letchworth	**B.** Wulfrath, Germany
3.	Buntingford	**C.** Neu-Isenburg, Germany
4.	Watford	**D.** Autun, France
5.	Sawbridgeworth	**E.** Alzey, Germany
6.	St. Albans	**F.** Franconville, France
7.	Ware	**G.** Kristiansund, Norway
8.	Hemel Hempstead	**H.** Luynes, France
9.	Harpenden	**I.** Worms, Germany
10.	Stevenage	**J** Bry-sur-Marne, France

QUIZ 34

GENERAL

1. Where in the county was Katherine, widow of Henry V, living when she had a son Edmund, by Owen Tudor? In due course Edmund had a son who became Henry VII, founder of the Tudor Dynasty.

2. Where, in 1751 (six years after the repeal of the law against witchcraft) were an elderly couple John and Ruth Osborn subjected to a so-called trial by ducking, in which the innocent drown and the guilty float, and are then punished by death? Ruth died immediately and John died three days later. One of the ringleaders of the ducking was hanged for murder.

3. Where in the southwest of the county is what is reputed to be the second largest medieval barn in England? Built between 1396 and 1401 it is 101 feet long and 40 feet wide. It is now owned by the County Council, and is occasionally opened to the public. (There are larger barns in the county but they are not medieval).

4. In which village in the east of the county are there Stocks and a Whipping Post on the grass

verge by the church gate, and on which village green in the west of the county are the same two forms of punishment?

5. Which town still has market pens which were used for sheep and pigs?

6. What is the Hertfordshire motto?

7. In which park in the west of the county is there a double row of lime trees known as 'King Charles Ride'? There is also the Nell Gwynne Monument, a tall obelisk built in the early 18th century, probably by the architect James Gibbs. Opinion differs as to whether the obelisk, which is without inscription, was to Nell Gwynne or her dog. Near by and built at the same time is a stone summerhouse. Nell Gwynne lived in a house by the park.

8. To the south of Wiggington is the 120-acre site of Champneys, with its parkland and mansion. What has it been used as since 1925, and is probably the most well known one in Britain?

9. Where is there a museum for an aircraft of the Second World War - the De Haviland Mosquito, a fast fighter-bomber?

10. Where in the county is there a lamppost museum?

3. MEDIEVAL BARN.

4. STOCKS AND WHIPPING
POST BY CHURCH GATE.

5. PIG AND SHEEP PENS.

QUIZ 35

BREWERIES

McMullen's of Hertford is now the only independent brewery in the county. There used to be many more. In 1818 there were still 75, and some of the main ones are listed below. Also listed are the towns or villages in which they were situated, but they are not against the correct brewery. Can you rearrange them correctly?

1. Fordhams	**A.** Royston
2. Christies	**B.** Bishops Stortford
3. Benskins	**C.** Baldock
4. Youngs	**D.** Furneux Pelham
5. Simpsons	**E.** Hitchin
6. Phillips	**F.** Ashwell
7. Taylors	**G.** Hoddesdon
8. Hawkes	**H.** Hertford
9. Lucas	**I.** Watford
10. Rayments	**J.** Sawbridgeworth

QUIZ 36

AND YET MORE PUBLIC HOUSES

See quiz 25

1. The Pig and Whistle   **A**. Essendon
2. The Spotted Dog   **B**. Perry Green
3. The Cat and Fiddle   **C**. Datchworth
4. The Chalkdrawer's Arms   **D**. Aston
5. The Hoops   **E**. Great Gaddesdon
6. The Candlestick   **F**. Flamstead
7. The Tally Ho   **G**. Gravesend, Albury
8. The Tilbury   **H**. Colney Heath
9. The Catherine Wheel   **I**. Barkway
10. The Cock and Bottle   **J**. Radlett

1. THE PIG AND WHISTLE.

3. THE CAT AND FIDDLE.

9. THE CATHERINE WHEEL.

QUIZ 37

PEOPLE – FAMOUS, NOTEWORTHY OR INFAMOUS

1. Which famous musician and conductor lived at Apple Tree Farm, Chorleywood, and died in Hitchin in 1944?
2. Which composer lived at Stagenhoe, a mansion near St. Pauls Walden during the 1880's
3. Which leading Quaker, who emigrated to America and had a state named after him, used to live in Basing House, 44 High Street, Rickmansworth?
4. Which great improver of British roads spent the last ten years of his life in Montague House, 68 High Street, Hoddesdon?
5. Which 17th century Protector spent his last thirty years in Cheshunt using the name of Clarke? There is an avenue named after him, and a close named after Mrs. Pengelly, the lady with whom he lived.
6. Which wealthy malster, and fanatical survivor of Cromwell's army owned Rye House in Hoddesdon? He was a leading conspirator in the plot to assassinate King Charles II and his brother, later King James II.

7. Who was the engineer responsible for constructing the New River, which was opened in 1613 to take drinking water from a spring at Great Amwell to London?

8. Ebenezer Albert Fox and Albert Ebenezer Fox were identical twins born at Symond's Green, near Stevenage in 1857, the sons of a Baptist preacher. They appeared regularly at court, but because of difficulty of identification were often acquitted. However between them they were convicted on no less than 220 occasions, and spent much time in prison. How did they mostly earn their living, and what type of offences were they committing?

9. James Lucas known as 'Mad Lucas,' lived at Elmwood House, Redcoats Green between Stevenage and Hitchin until 17th April 1874, why is he remembered?

10. Clibbon's Post is on the side of the road between Bull's Green and Bramfield to mark the spot where Walter Clibbon was killed on 28th December 1782. What was he doing when he was killed?

QUIZ 38

HAILEYBURY SCHOOL

1. Haileybury is a leading Public School in the county. Where is it?
2. Before the present school was built there had been a college on the site. What date was the college first established?
3. Who was it for?
4. When was the present school built?
5. Who designed it, and is well known as the designer of the National Gallery in Trafalgar Square?
6. Which 'Old Boy' of the former college, while Governor General of the Punjab, led an army of Sikhs in a three month siege to retake Delhi during the Indian Mutiny. He later became Governor General of India, and received a peerage. A house in the present school is named after him?
7. Which 'Old Boy' of the present school became a General and served in France from 1914 to 1917, and then in 1918 conquered Palestine and Syria in a rapid and brilliant campaign. There is also a house named after him?
8. How many 'Old Boys' lost their lives in the First World War?

9. What do these four 'Old Boys' have in common: Clifford Coffin, Cyril Frisbby, Rupert Hallowes and Clement Robertson?
10. Which former Prime Minister was a pupil at the school?

QUIZ 39

CHURCHES

1. Which Hertfordshire parish church, built in 1838, was the first of many throughout England to be designed by Sir George Gilbert Scott, who is best remembered for The Albert Memorial and St. Pancras Station hotel?
2. In which village churchyard is Field Marshall Earl Alexander of Tunis buried?
3. In which parish church is there a plaque set up by the Chinese Minister in London, to commemorate the life of Scottish surgeon Sir James Cantlie who died in 1926? He had spent many years in China and India studying tropical illnesses, and he founded the Royal Society for Tropical Medicine.
4. Where is the only church in the county dedicated to St. Dunstan?
5. Which parish church was badly damaged by bombs dropped by a Zeppelin in September 1916? Inside it has a christening bowl that was made by the renowned potter Josiah Wedgwood.
6. Which parish church has the oldest bell in the county?

7. There is only one church in the county, a Roman Catholic Church that is dedicated to St. Richard. Where is it?
8. In which parish since 1984 has the Anglian church of St. Andrew also been the Roman Catholic Church of The Holy Cross? It has a head of a king and a queen by Henry Moore on either side of the west door, and a Tree of Life, designed by him in a window over the door. Inside is a quilt made by the Women's Institute and presented to Queen Mary on her Silver Jubilee in 1935. There is also a wonderful collection of over 200 canvas-embroidered hassocks.
9. Which parish church, built in 1778, has the design of a classical Greek Temple, and is a copy of the Temple of Apollo at Delos?
10. Quite apart from the outward appearance of the above church, how does the internal layout differ from any other church in the county and possibly in England?

1. THE FIRST CHURCH BUILT BY
SIR GEORGE GILBERT SCOTT.

2. EARL ALEXANDER'S GRAVE.

4. ST. DUNSTAN.

9. PARISH CHURCH BUILT LIKE
THE TEMPLE OF APOLLO AT DELOS.

QUIZ 40

GENERAL

1. In which village in the north of the county is there a former Merchant Taylors School dated 1681, a sturdy clunch built lock-up and a long, high thatched cob wall?

2. In Braughing the 2nd October is known as 'Old Man's Day,' and the church funeral bell is tolled, and later in the evening the bells are rung again. Why is this?

3. When and where did the last trams run within Hertfordshire?

4. When the trams ceased to run, what replaced them, and for how long?

5. Nasty sounds rather an unpleasant place name. In which parish is the hamlet of Nasty?

6. What was the former alternative name of the river Mimram?

7. By which name was Kings Langley known until its close association with royalty in the 12th and 13th centuries?

8. Another village that has had a name change is St. Pauls Walden. By which name was it known until 1544?

9. Where on a common in the south west of the county, is a pond known as 'The Apostles

118

Pond,' because twelve lime trees representing the twelve apostles surround it?

10. In Preston, a large Queen Anne house, Temple Disney dating from 1714 (on the site of a former Knights Templar building), was greatly enlarged by Lutyens in 1908. What is it used as now?

CLUNCH BUILT LOCK-UP AND
THATCHED COB WALL.

QUIZ 41

INDUSTRIES – PAST AND PRESENT

1. John Dickinson set up Apsley Mills at Hemel Hempstead, and Nash Mills and Croxley Mills, near Watford, in the early 19th century and pioneered the production of which commodity, which is still being produced by those mills?

2. What was produced by David Evans and Company at Tring for most of the 19th century, and at Abbey Mills, St. Albans, until the 1930's?

3. Which Hertfordshire town was, from the middle ages until the last century, the foremost malting town in Britain?

4. For which modern industry are Elstree and Borehamwood noted?

5. Which cottage industry was widespread among the women in the Hitchin area, and northwest of the county, in the 18th and 19th centuries?

6. At Weston, near Baldock, in one small workshop, a unique industry is still carried on, using material imported from Canada. What is it?

7. What, until recent times, was the main industry over a very large area of the Lea Valley in the southeast of the county?
8. In 1914 the landlord of the Raven Inn at Hexton started an ancillary business, which grew into a thriving industry. Who was he and what was the product?
9. Which industry was carried on at Ayot House, Ayot, St. Lawrence for some years after the Second World War?
10. Which 'industry' is now flourishing in Royston? The open space of Therfield Heath play a major part in it.

QUIZ 42

AND MORE VILLAGE PUBLIC HOUSES

See Quiz 25

1.	The Valiant Trooper	**A.** Lemsford
2.	The Farmers Boy	**B.** Park Street
3.	The Bushel and Strike	**C.** Amwell, Wheathampstead
4.	The Countryman	**D.** Aldbury
5.	The Horns	**E.** Chapmore End
6.	The Crooked Chimney	**F.** Hailey, Hoddesden
7.	The Galley Hall	**G.** Chipping
8.	The Overdraught	**H.** Ashwell
9.	The Elephant and Castle	**I.** Brickendon
10.	The Woodman	**J.** Bulls Green, Datchworth

4. THE COUNTRYMAN.

6. THE CROOKED CHIMNEY.

7. THE GALLEY HALL.

9. THE ELEPHANT AND CASTLE.

QUIZ 43

MORE NOTEWORTHY HERTFORDIANS

1. Which great lawyer and philosopher, born in 1651, who became Lord Chancellor to William III, and framed the Declaration of Rights, lived at Brookmans, Welham Green? His large tomb in North Mymms Church remembers him.

2. One of two Puritan brothers from Widford who emigrated to America? He became known as the Indian Apostle, as he was the first person to preach to them in their own language. He was one of the founders of Harvard University.

3. Who, born in Ardeley, became vicar of Ware, but later emigrated to America and in 1656 became the first President of Harvard University?

4. Which famous admiral and circumnavigator of the world lived at Moor Park, Rickmansworth, until his death in 1762?

5. Which future Prime Minister was returned as Member of Parliament for Hertford in 1874?

6. Who were the two German born Jewish brothers who made their fortunes out of diamond mining in South Africa? They were bachelors and very generous philanthropists.

They lived in Tewin Water, a white mansion overlooking the River Mimram. One died in 1906 and the other in 1930 and both were buried in Tewin churchyard. The elder of the two had been a close colleague of Cecil Rhodes in South Africa and Rhodesia, and there is a bridge across the Zambesi named after the younger one.

7. Which well-known Lord Mayor of London was Lord of the Manor of Thorley from 1399-1413?

8. During the Second World War who lived at Ayot House, Ayot St. Lawrence?

9. In which town, where his father was vicar, was Cecil Rhodes, the founder of Rhodesia born in 1853? There is now a Cecil Rhodes Memorial Museum there.

10. Which French Count lived incognito for many years in Harpenden, using the name Count de Villemont?

QUIZ 44

MORE TOWN TWINNING

Again the Hertfordshire towns do not have their correct 'twin' town listed opposite to them. Can you sort them out?

1.	Royston	**A.** Dinant, Belgium
2.	Radlett	**B.** Evron, France
3.	Cheshunt	**C.** Zierikzee, Holland
4.	Borehamwood	**D.** Villiers-sur-Marne, France
5.	Hatfield	**E.** Grossalmerode, Germany
6.	Hitchin	**F.** Louveciennes, France
7.	Baldock	**G.** Stains, France
8.	Hertford	**H.** Fontenay-aux-Roses, France
9.	Hoddesdon	**I.** Eisenberg, Germany
10.	Bishops Storford	**J.** Bingen-am-Rhein, Germany

QUIZ 45

GENERAL

1. What is the area of Hertfordshire (in square miles)?
2. Which is the highest point in the county?
3. Which is most southerly village in the county?
4. Which is the most northerly?
5. Which is the most westerly?
6. Which is the longest river in the county?
7. The National Trust owns only two sites in the county, which are open to the public. Where are they?
8. Great Munden has not always been so called. It has had two previous names, what were they?
9. Which is thought to be the oldest red-bricked building in the county?
10. Which Hertfordshire gateway was used in the opening scenes of the long running television series 'Porridge'?

QUIZ 46

ODD ONE OUT

In the following groups of names, three have one thing in common the fourth does not. Which is the odd one out?

1.   Chells   Broadwater
       Haldens   Shephall
2.   Akeman   Icknield
       Ermine   Watling
3.   Hormead   Stocking
       Brent   Furneux
4.   Garston   Adeyfields
       Bennetts End   Counters End
5.   Berkhamsted Castle Hertford Castle
       Ravensburgh Castle Anstey Castle
6.   Dacorum   Uttlesford
       Three Rivers   Hertsmere
7.   Handside   Peartree
       Woodhall   Hartham
8.   Wilstone   Stockers
       Marsworth   Startops End
9.   Oxlease   Townsend
       Fleetville   Marshalswick
10.   Beane   Gade
11.   Rib   Mimram

130

QUIZ 47

GENERAL

1. Where in the county is Temple Bar, the gateway designed by Sir Christopher Wren, which used to bestraddle Fleet Street as one of the gateways leading into the City of London?
2. In which village is the headquarters of the Society for Krishna Conciousness (Hare Krishna sect)?
3. Until it became a restaurant, which was thought to be the oldest licensed inn in the county, dating back to 1279?
4. The reason why the famed eleven feet square Great Bed of Ware was made is rather vague. Who was the carpenter who made it?
5. When and where was it last in Hertfordshire?
6. Where is it now?
7. Which almost unique buildings are to be seen along the River Lea at Ware?
8. A Buntingford man, who was a carrier from Cambridge to London, also hired out horses. He gave his customers no choice as to which horse they had, making them always take the one nearest to the stable door, so that the horses were worked in turn. This practice gave rise to a well-known saying, and although the

man died in 1630 the saying is still used today. Who was he, and what was the saying?

9. Who was the legendary 'Dragon Slayer' of Brent Pelham, who in 1086 was buried under the wall of the church, as the devil had vowed to have his body if he was buried within the church, or in the churchyard, as a revenge for him having killed one of his dragons?

10. In which village, in the north of the county, can you see a large, listed, red-bricked, octagonal dovecote?

3. THE FORMER LICENSED INN DATING BACK TO 1279.

10. OCTAGONAL DOVECOTE.

133

QUIZ 48

PUBLIC HOUSES NAMED AFTER PEOPLE

Ten Public Houses named after people, real or imaginary, are listed below, but they are not shown opposite their correct town or village. Can you pair them up correctly?

1. The Queen Adelaide
2. The Lord Haig
3. The Lord Louis
4. The Hermit of Redcoats
5. Anne of Cleves
6. The John Bunyan
7. The Garibaldi
8. The John Gilpin
9. The Sir John Barleycorn
10. The Sir Robert Peel

A. Coleman Green
B. St. Albans
C. Ware
D. Hitchin
E. Watford
F. Shenley
G. Broxbourne
H. Stanstead Abbots
I. Hertford
J. Titmore Green

1. THE QUEEN ADELAIDE.

3. THE LORD LOUIS.

4. THE HERMIT OF REDCOADS.

6. THE JOHN BUNYAN.

8. THE JOHN GILPIN.

QUIZ 49

GENERAL

1. In which village does the sign of the White Horse public house depict a headless horse, in keeping with a legend of a local lane being haunted by a headless horse?

2. On which village green is there a well-preserved metal capped whipping post, with a plaque with the following inscription, 'This Whipping Post was last known to be used on July 27th 1665 when two vagabonds were publicly flogged here'?

3. Who was the grocer and churchwarden, who on his death in 1724, had his coffin put in the rafters of an outhouse behind his shop in the High Street in Stevenage, so that body snatchers would be unable to get his body? The premises of the shop are now the National Westminster Bank.

4. In which village in 1725 did John Rivers start a fruit nursery, and developed fruit, which was widely grown? A plum and a nectarine both named 'Early Rivers,' are two of the varieties that are still grown today.

5. In which churchyard in the north of the county is the 'grave' of the legendary giant Jack O'Legs, who made his living as a robber, and

if legend is to be believed, befriended and helped the poor?

6. When and where was the last highwayman shot in this county?

7. On 11th March 1802' Robert Snooks was the last highwayman to be hanged in England. As no one would pay for a coffin, he was buried by the hangman under the gallows on the common. The grave is now marked by two white Stones. Where is it?

8. In the 1920's and 1930's, before it became famous as a road junction, for what was Bricket Wood well known?

9. The town of Baldock was first built by the Knights Templar. After which Middle East town is it thought to be named?

10. Which town in the north east of the county has a recently restored, redbrick lock-up, which is furnished with a bed, a candle, a plate and a tankard?

1. HEADLESS HORSE PUBLIC HOUSE SIGN.

2. WHIPPING POST.

5. STONES MARKING GRAVE OF JACK O'LEGS.

10. RESTORED RED BRICK LOCK-UP.

QUIZ 50

CHURCHES

1. Consecrated in 1906, in which town is the fine Roman Catholic Church of St. Joseph and the Holy Martyrs, with memorials to the men who lost their lives in both World Wars incorporated into the sanctuary?

2. Which unusual features for Hertfordshire churches do the following all have, St. Thomas the Martyr, Northaw, St. Lawrence, Bovington, St Mary Magdalene, Barkway and St. John the Baptist, Royston?

3. What do St. Andrew, Buckland, St. Mary, Little Hormead, St. James, Stanstead Abbots and Oxhey Chapel all have in common?

4. Which external architectural feature, unusual in Norman churches in Hertfordshire can be seen on only three of the Norman churches within the county? They are St. John the Baptist, Great Amwell, St. Leonard, Bengeo, and St. Mary the Virgin, Great Wymondley. (Some later churches have one.)

5. In which parish are there two lych-gates, one leading into the churchyard and church, which was built to commemorate the Diamond Jubilee of Queen Victoria, and the other, leading into a churchyard on the other side of

road, which was erected as a memorial to those who died in the First World War, and now also commemorates those who died in the Second World War?

6. Which is the only church in the county still to have part of a medieval 'Doom Painting' (a painting showing what could happen to evil-doers at the Last Judgement)? Also in the church is a fine marble effigy of Francis Bacon, who is buried in the chancel.

7. There are very few churches in England dedicated to St. Cecilia. One of them is in Hertfordshire. In which parish is it?

8. A 'Jesse Window' is a stained glass window showing the ancestral tree of Jesus Christ back to Jesse (father of David). The only example in the county is part of a 14th century window. Which church is this in?

9. Which is the smallest parish church in the county, it has been unused since 1975 and is falling into disrepair?

10. Roman Catholic churches are all comparatively modern. Which is the oldest one in Hertfordshire?

1. ST. JOSEPH AND THE HOLY MARTYRS.

7. ST. CECILIA.

9. UNUSED SINCE 1975, THIS IS THE SMALLEST
PARISH CHURCH IN HERTFORDSHIRE.

QUIZ 51

THOROUGHFARES

In every town there are some main thoroughfares with unusual or outstanding names. In which towns are the following groups.

1. Bucklersbury   Bancroft
   Payne's Park   Tilehouse Street
2. The Campus   Howardsgate
   Parkway   Howlands
3. The Causeway   Hockerill Street
   Havers Lane   Northgate End
4. Darkes Lane   Mutton Lane
   Billy Lows Lane   The Walk
5. Lytton Way   Martins Way
   Gunnels Wood Road   Fairlands Way
6. Cowbridge   Bull Plain
   Gascoigne Way   Old Cross
7. Exchange Road   Gammons Lane
   Whippendell Road   Beechen Grove
8. Marlowes   Queensway
   Piccotts End   Adeyfield Road
9. Icknield Way   Pixmore Way
   Leys Avenue   Broadway
10. Elstree Way   Cranes Way
    Fursehill Road   Manor Way

QUIZ 52

AND MORE CHURCHES

1. In which town is St. Mary's, a majestic Norman church, begun in about 1140 and completed about 40 years later? The central tower with tall leaded spire rise to nearly 200 feet. Also notable is the contemporary clerestory, a rare feature.

2. In which town is All Saints, a large late 19th century church built of red Runcorn stone? It was built to replace an earlier church, which was burned down. The tower was added in 1905, and has the inscription 'In memory of the glorious reign of our beloved Queen Victoria.'

3. Just to the South of London Colney, close to the M25, is a magnificent ecclesiastical building, restored in 1964 from a former convent and much admired by Sir John Betjeman. What is the building?

4. Which brick built parish church, designed in 1914 by Sir Edward Lutyens, is noted for the eaves, which project far over the walls? It has no tower, but a small bell turret, and the interior is in complete contrast to traditional design.

5. In an almost deserted village, which parish church with a stair turret on the tower, claims

to be the highest church above sea level in the county?

6. What do All Saints church, Radwell, St. Margaret's Church, Stocking Pelham, and St. Margaret of Antioch Church, Bygrave have in common?

7. Which parish church has inscribed on the tower 'TIME FLIES MIND YOUR BUSINESS'?

8. Which parish church in the West of the county is unusual with a chequered tower of alternate flint and stone squares? Inside there is a plaque commemorating the fact that all the men from the parish who went to fight in the First World War came home safely. The only parish in the county, where this is so?

9. Where is the Anglican Church in the county dedicated to St. Helen?

10. In which town is St. Mary's, a 14th century wide and roomy church with a broad tower and two-storied porch? A clerestory was added in the 15th century and the interior is rich in carvings. Pevsner described it as 'A wealthy town church.'

4. CHURCH DESIGNED BY SIR EDWARD LUTYENS.

TIME FLIES – MIND YOUR BUSINESS.

5. CHURCH CLAIMING TO BE
HIGHEST ABOVE SEA LEVEL.

8. CHEQUERED TOWER.

QUIZ 53

GENERAL

1. Which Public House in Hatfield is thought to be the inn referred to by Charles Dickens, when he tells how Bill Sykes fled from London, and was discovered in Hatfield, in the story of Oliver Twist?

2. Where is there a large, castellated 'Folly Arch,' possibly once the gateway to an estate, built by Sir Jeremy Sambrooke, owner of a nearby house?

3. Where is there another castellated folly Stratton's Folly, a red brick, 100 foot tower, built in 1789 by retired admiral John Stratton in the hope that he could stand on the battlements and see ships go along the Thames, but he would have been unable to do so? It is now lived in.

4. Another folly - this time dug 70 feet into a hillside - Scott's Grotto. It is full of small rooms and passages all lined with shells of all shapes and sizes. After visiting it Dr. Johnson described it as a 'Fairy Palace.' Where is it?

5. Charles Lamb spent much time visiting his Grandmother at Blakesware, near Widford, where she was housekeeper. He also used to visit his Great Aunt (his Grandmother's sister)

who was also a housekeeper at a mansion northwest of Wheathampstead. What was the name of the house?

6. How did the district of Dacorum get its name?
7. Which is the oldest Golf Club in the county?
8. Many villages still have a pump, although none of them are working. Which village in the west of the county has an unusual large, circular pump on the village green?
9. How did Royston get its name?
10. In which north Hertfordshire village is there an imposing clock tower war memorial that was provided by the Clutterbuck family in memory of Major Clutterbuck and twelve other local men who were killed in the First World?

2. CASTELLATED 'FOLLY ARCH.'

8. CIRCULAR PUMP.

10. CLOCK TOWER – WAR MEMORIAL.

QUIZ 54

AND MORE CHURCHES

1. Which parish church has bench ends carved in Baroque style by the renowned wood carver Joseph Mayer of Oberammergau (Germany), who had been invited to England by Earl Cowper?

2. Which external features, unusual for Hertfordshire churches, do the following all have: All Saints, Datchworth, St. Paul, Hunton Bridge, St. Matthew, Oxhey, St. Peter, Ayot St. Peter, St. Helen, Wheathampstead and St. Leonard, Sandridge?

3. Which external feature, usually by the door, and mostly incomplete, may still be seen on a few churches within the county including St. Mary, Redbourn, St. Mary, North Mimms, St. Margaret, Ridge, St. Mary the Virgin, Great Wymondley, and St. Leonard, Sandridge?

4. Which parish church is renowned for its collection of stained glass by the 'Pre-Raphaelites,' including William Morris, Ford Madox Brown, Philip Webb, Selwyn Image, Dante Gabriel Rossetti and a particularly fine window by Sir Edward Burne-Jones?

5. Which parish church in the north of the county is noted externally for its possibly 15th century

double lych-gate and a two storied south porch of the same century, and a tall buttressed tower with steeple on an octagonal drum; and internally for medieval graffiti bewailing the plague, and a picture of old St. Pauls scratched into the wall of the tower?

6. In which parish is St. James the Great, with its unusual round, tall, slim tower and spire complete with clock, said to be a replica of a fisherman's church at Great Yarmouth (Saint James is the Patron Saint of fishermen)?

7. During the 17th and 18th centuries box pews (enclosed seating to give privacy to the occupants) were installed in many churches. Some had low sides and some high. There are still a few churches in the county with low box pews, but which is the only parish church with high ones?

8. There is only one parish church in the county dedicated to St. Katherine (not Catherine). Where is it?

9. St. Etheldra's church in Chesfield was demolished in 1750. There is now only one church in the county dedicated to this saint. Where is it?

10. Which church in the county is built within the bailey of a former castle?

5. DOUBLE LYCH-GATE.

6. ST. JAMES THE GREAT.

10. REMAINS OF CASTLE MOTTE AND
CHURCH WITHIN THE FORMER BAILEY.

QUIZ 55

PUBLIC HOUSES WITH ANIMAL NAMES

Throughout the county there are public houses with animal names. Ten of the more unusual ones are listed below, but they are not opposite their correct town or village. Can you pair them up correctly? Where a town is shown twice there are two of the listed public houses in that town.

1.	The Hedgehog	**A.** Stevenage
2.	The March Hare	**B.** Hertford
3.	The Brown Bear	**C.** Cheshunt
4.	The White Bear	**D.** Bengeo
5.	The Ram	**E.** Welwyn Garden City
6.	The Squirrel	**F.** Eastwick
7.	The Crocodile	**G.** Stevenage
8.	The Sow and Pigs	**H.** Royston
9.	The Greyhound	**I.** Braughing
10.	The Lion	**J.** Thundridge

2. THE MARCH HARE.

5. THE RAM.

7. THE CROCODILE.

8. THE SOW AND PIGS.

10. THE LION.

QUIZ 56

MORE TOWN AND VILLAGE TWINNING

As some Hertfordshire towns are twinned to more than one continental town, some of the Hertfordshire towns listed below will have appeared on a previous page. As before the Hertfordshire towns do not have their correct 'twin' opposite them. Can you sort them out?

1.	St. Albans	**A.**	Viernheim, Germany
2.	Bishops Stortford	**B.**	Cosne-sur-le-Loire, France
3.	Borehamwood	**C.**	Nuits St. Georges, France
4.	Colney Heath	**D.**	Chagny, France
5.	Harpenden	**E.**	Nevers, France
6.	Radlett	**F.**	Inglehein, Germany
7.	Potters Bar	**G.**	Boissy, France
8.	Stevenage	**H.**	Offenburg, Germany
9.	Hitchin	**I.**	Friedburg, Germany
10.	Letchworth	**J.**	Germiende Lauteraz, Germany

QUIZ 57

GENERAL

1. Letchworth was the first Garden City. When was it started?
2. Welwyn Garden City was next. When was that started?
3. Before the Second World War many villages had a large, round, yellow A.A. sign on a prominent building showing the name of the village. It also showed the distance to a nearby town or village in each direction, and the distance to London. They were taken down at the outbreak of war so that in the event of invasion they would not help the enemy to find their whereabouts. Which is the only village in the county now to have one of these signs?
4. In which village is the Plough Public House that now houses the magnificent Compton organ that was in the Gaumont cinema in North Finchley until it closed in 1967?
5. Which village was the home of the much-depicted Ovaltine Farm with its neat black and white thatched buildings?
6. Which village has its War Memorial in the form of a small shrine in a garden by the church gate? Opposite is a village green with a

covered well, surrounded by white walled thatched houses, with a village hall to match, they were built in 1917 by the Lord of the Manor as a welcome home to men from the parish who had been fighting in the First World War.

7. The parish of Brickendon is entitled to use an additional name as a result of exemption from certain taxes granted to it by Henry II. What is the name?

8. Milestones generally were first placed along our roads by the Turnpike Trusts from 1742 onwards, but in which village is there a large 6 feet high milestone that was set up some 12 years earlier, and bearing the crescent of Trinity College, Cambridge, and showing the distances to Cambridge, Ware and London? It is the southernmost of four that were set up in the county to assist travellers to Cambridge.

9. Where in Hertfordshire are there milestones, or short metal posts, showing the distance to Braunston in Northamptonshire?

10. In which village, are the only two Public Houses, named the Malta and the Gibraltar Castle?

6. COVERED WELL AND THATCHED COTTAGES.

8. SIX FOOT HIGH MILESTONE.

9. METAL MILEPOST.

QUIZ 58

TOWNS AND VILLAGES
BEGINNING WITH B

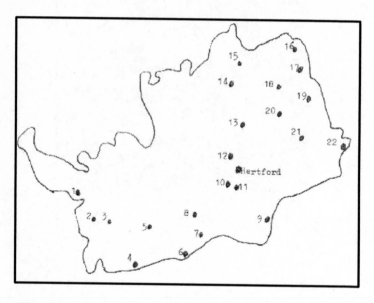

The twenty-two dots on the map all represent a town or village beginning with the letter B.

How many can you name?

QUIZ 59

VILLAGES BEGINNING WITH A VOWEL

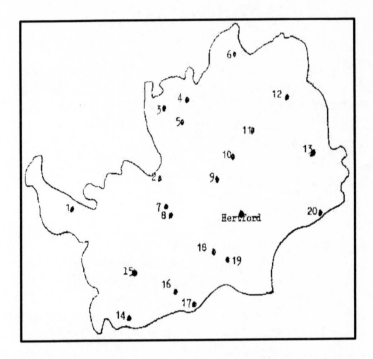

The twenty dots on the map all represent a village.
The name of all of them begins with a vowel.

How many can you name?

QUIZ 60

PUBLIC HOUSES
WITH BIRD NAMES

Ten Public Houses with bird names are listed below, but they are not shown opposite their correct town or village. Can you pair them up correctly? Where towns are shown twice there are two listed Public Houses in each town.

1.	The Nightingale	**A.** St. Albans
2.	The Raven	**B.** Hemel Hempstead
3.	The Peacock	**C.** Hitchin
4.	The Three Moorhens	**D.** Standon
5.	The Kingfisher	**E.** St. Albans
6.	The Goldcrest	**F.** Park Street
7.	The Peahen	**G.** Broxbourne
8.	The Heron	**H.** Hitchin
9.	The Falcon	**I.** Hexton
10.	The Three Blackbirds	**J.** Baldock

1. THE NIGHTINGALE.

2. THE RAVEN.

3. THE PEACOCK.

5. THE KINGFISHER.

6. THE GOLDCREST.

ANSWER SECTION

1) ROMAN HERTFORDSHIRE

1, Cassivelaunus, 'King' of the Catuvellauni. 2, Julius Caesar. 3, About 45 A.D. 4, Queen Boudica (Boadicea). 5, Watling Street. 6, Akeman Street. 7, Ermine Street. 8, Stane Street. 9, Braughing (to the north of Puckeridge). 10, Under the Al (M) by Welwyn.

2) KINGS AND QUEENS

1, James I. 2, Richard II. 3, Henry VIII. 4, Hunsdon. 5, Ashridge. 6, Hatfield Palace - traditionally sitting under an oak tree. 7, James I. 8, Henry VI. 9, Queen Victoria. 10, St. Pauls Waldenbury.

3) GENERAL

1, St. Albans. 2, Langley Palace. 3, Henry VIII married Ann Boleyn. 4, St. Albans. 5, He proclaimed Lady Jane Grey 'Queen.' 6, Theobalds. 7, Ashwell, Hertford, Berkhamsted, St. Albans and Stansted Abbots. 8, Roman Catholic Archbishop and Cardinals of Westminster. 9, At Wadesmill on the Old North Road - Ermine Street (now the A10). 10, He was the original compiler of old Moore's Almanac.

4) CASTLES

1, Berkhamsted. 2, Pirton. 3, Wymondley. 4, Walkern. 5, Benington. 6, Therfield. 7, Anstey. 8, South Mimms. 9, Hertford. 10, Waytemore.

5) CASTLES

1, Berkhamsted. 2, Hertford. 3, Berkhamsted. 4, Anstey. 5, Bishops Stortford. 6, Hertford. 7, Berkhamsted. 8, Benington. 9, Hertford. 10, Berkhamsted.

6) CASTLES

1, Berkhamsted. 2, Queen Elizabeth I in 1593. 3, Benington. 4, Waytemore. 5, Waytemore. 6, Pirton. 7, Anstey. 8, As a training college by the East India Trading Company. 9, Berkhamsted. 10, Anstey.

7) HUNDREDS

1, Hitchin. 2, Broadwater. 3, Odsey. 4, Edwinstree. 5, Braughing. 6, Hertford. 7, Cashio. 8, Dacorum.

8) ST ALBANS CATHEDRAL

1, Offa, King of Mercia. 2, 1088. 3. A Watching Chamber from which monks kept a continual watch over the shrine of St. Alban. 4,Lord Grimthrope. 5, The Martyrdom of St. Alban. 6, Humphrey, Duke of Gloucester, son of Henry IV. 7, Abbot Thomas de la

Mare. 8, Sir George Gilbert Scott. 9, Her Majesty The Queen. 10, The Centenary of Laporte, PLC of Luton.

9) ST ALBANS CATHEDRAL

1, 1877. 2, Thomas Legh Claughton. 3, Matthew. Mark, Luke and John. 4, Lord Aldenham. 5, Sixty-five. 6, Alfred Gilbert - better known for his Eros in Piccadilly Circus. 7, Illuminated book of Remembrance for the 12,778 men and 3 women of the diocese who lost their lives in the First World War. 8, St. Alban. 9, Mother's Union. 10, An astronomical clock, worked by weights and an elaborate gearing system.

10) HOUSES

1. Hatfield House. 2, Cassiobury Park. 3, Knebworth. 4, Gorhambury. 5, Moor Park. 6, Ashridge. 7, Standon Lordship. 8, Brocket Hall. 9, Rye House, Hoddesdon. 10, Panshanger.

11) HATFIELD HOUSE

1. Bishop of Ely. 2, John Morton, Archbishop of Canterbury. 3, Sir Robert Cecil, First Earl of Salisbury. 4, Four years -1611. 5, E shaped, in honour of Queen Elizabeth I. 6, Queen Elizabeth I. 7, Burnt to death after a fire was started by a candle in her bedroom. 8, The Third Marquis of Salisbury - three times Conservative Prime Minister. 9, Sir George Frampton. 10, Used as a Military Hospital.

12) DISTRICT COUNCILS

1. Dacorum. 2, Three Rivers. 3. Watford. 4, St. Albans. 5, Hertsmere. 6, North Hertfordshire. 7. Welwyn-Hatfield. 8, Stevenage. 9, East Hertfordshire. 10, Broxbourne.

13) CHURCHES AND OTHER RELIGIOUS BUILDINGS

1, St. Mary, Hitchin. 2, Railway Street, Hertford. 3, Mosques. 4, Synagogues. 5, Church of the Holy Road, Market Street, Watford. 6, St. Leonard, Bengeo. 7. Newnham. 8, Oxhey. 9, Bishops Stortford. 10, Borehamwood.

14) FAMOUS PEOPLE

1, Sir William Herkomer. 2, Sir John Bennet Lawes. 3, William Cowper. 4, John Scott. 5, Henry Moore. 6, Eileen Soper. 7, Ellen Terry. 8, Eric Morecombe. 9, Ebenezer Howard. 10, Thomas Dimsdale.

15) PUBLIC HOUSES

1, Stevenage. 2, St. Albans. 3, Hemel Hempstead. 4, Watford. 5, Royston 6, Cheshunt. 7, Bishops Stortford. 8, Hitchin. 9, Hertford. 10, Ware.

16) RAILWAYS

1, The London and Birmingham Railway. 2, Tring Cutting, it is 2½ miles long and 57 feet deep. It was dug by hand, and the earth removed by wheelbarrows. Six men were killed during its construction. 3, Bishops Stortford. 4, Buntingford. 5, The Southbury Loop running through Theobalds Grove. 6, Lewis Cubitt. 7, Thomas Brassey. 8, 98 feet high with 40 arches. 9, Royston. 10, Rickmansworth.

17) GENERAL

1, Icknield Way. 2, Ravensburgh Castle. 3, Grimm's Ditch. 4, Devil's Dyke. 5, Arbury Banks. 6, Wilbury Hill. 7, A cave, beehive shaped and unique in Britain. The origin of it is not known, but Christian symbols scratched into the walls may show a connection with the Knights Templar who was known to have been in that area, but it is believed to be much older. 8, Batchwood Hall, St. Albans. 9, Cardinal Wolsey. 10, Cromer.

18) INDUSTRIES - PAST AND PRESENT

1, Paper. 2, Lavender, which was distilled into Lavender Water. 3, Bells, but he did also make clocks. 4, Standon. 5, Growing watercress. 6, Indoor Plants. 7, Bricks. He made bricks which were larger than the standard brick, and they were interlocking. 8, Fruit growers - Lane's Prince Albert is still a popular cooking apple. 9, Tanners and leather dressers. 10. Diesel rail cars and carriages.

19) PEOPLE - FAMOUS, NOTEWORTHY OR INFAMOUS

1, Piers Gaveston. 2, Lady Caroline Lamb. 3, Lord Byron. 4, Nell Gwynne. 5, Highway Robbery. 6, Admiral Byng. 7, Witchcraft. 8, Sir Henry Chauncey. 9, Robert Clutterbuck. 10, Married at 16 she had 39 children (only one set of twins), 7 boys and 32 girls. All reached adulthood and the youngest son became a surgeon. The last was born when she was 54, and she died about ten years later.

20) MORE PUBLIC HOUSES

1, Baldock. 2, Harpenden. 3, Hoddesdon. 4, Tring. 5,Potters Bar. 6, Berkhamsted. 7, Sawhridgeworth. 8, Welwyn Garden City. 9, Buntingford. 10, Hatfield.

21) MONUMENTS AND MEMORIALS

1, John Bunyan. 2, He shot down a Schutte-Lanz airship on 2nd September 1916. It was the first German airship (and is often referred to as a Zeppelin) to he destroyed in Britain. 3, The Third Duke of Bridgewater, the 'Canal Duke,' a pioneer of canals in Britain. 4, 'The abolition of slavery.' Until his death in 1846 Clarkson worked closely with William Wilberforce to secure the abolition of the slave trade. 5, It was erected in 1901 to commemorate the reign of Queen Victoria, and was restored in 1977 to commemorate the Silver Jubilee of Queen Elizabeth II. 6, They were both members of the newly formed Royal Flying Corps, and were killed when their Deperdussin plane crashed during a training flight. 7, The first manned balloon flight over England. Lunardi ascended from the Artillery Ground in Finshury, in London, and after briefly touching down at Welham Green just long enough to hand out his cat and his dog, he continued his flight until he finally landed in a field at Standon Green End. 8, King Edward I. He had a similar stone cross erected at all the overnight stopping places whilst he was bringing the body of his Queen, Eleanor, back to London after she had died at Harby, near Lincoln in 1290. 9, The building of the New River, a canal to take water from Amwell (and later from Chadwell) to London. 10, At Nuthampstead.

22) HOUSES

1, Theobalds. 2, Tring Park. 3, Holywell. 4, The Grove. 5, Goldings. 6, North Mimms Park. 7, Bishops Palace, Much Hadham. 8, Langleybury. 9, Tittenhanger. 10, Little Hadham Hall.

23) GENERAL

1, Ware, in Place House off East Street. 2, Letchmore Heath. 3, In Hertford on 10th April, 1876 when George Hill was hanged for the murder of his son. 4, In Madame Tussauds in London. 5, St. Albans - 1915

(Hertford gaol closed in 1879). 6, Shenley. 7, Barley. 8, The Gunpowder Plot to blow up the Houses of Parliament in 1605. 9. St. Joan of Arc Convent School, Rickmansworth. 10, Stevenage.

24) NOTEWORTHY HERTFORDIANS

1, Viceroy of India. 2, Suffragette. 3, Sir Thomas More. 4, Sir Richard Fanshawe. 5, Sir Ralph Sadleir. 6, Sir Henry Bessemer. 7, He became Pope - Adrian IV - the only Englishman ever to do so. 8, William Plumer. 9, Lionel Walter 2nd Baron Rothschild. 10, Viscount Herbert Gladstone.

25) VILLAGE PUBLIC HOUSES

1, H. 2, D. 3, I. 4, B. 5, A. 6, G. 7, C. 8, J. 9, E. 10, F.

26) CHURCHES AND CHURCHYARDS

1, All Saints, Kings Langley. 2, St. Mary, Wallington. 3, Bramfield. 4, Church of the Holy Cross, Sarratt. 5, Stevenage. 6, St. John the Evangelist, High Cross. 7, St. Leonard, Flamstead. 8, Anstey. 9, St. Ippolytys, Ippollitts. 10, St Mary, Northchurch.

27) GENERAL

1, In his Palace at Royston. 2, Therfield Heath. 3, Bedwell. 4, Northaw – 1917. 5, Hertford. 6, The Roebuck. 7, Samuel Pepys. 8, Watford. 9, Vicarage Road. 10. Metropolitan.

28) AUTHORS

1, Sir Edward Bulwer-Lytton. 2, George Bernard Shaw, 3, Charles Lamb. 4, Anthony Trollope. 5, E.M. Forster. 6, Rebecca West. 7, Grahame Greene. 8, Capt. W.E. Johns (Author of the Biggle's Books). 9, Beatrix Potter - Peter Rabbit in Mr. McGregor's Garden. 10. Dame Barbara Cartland.

29) RIVERS

1, Chess. 2, Gade. 3, Bulbourne. 4, Ver. 5, Colne. 6, Lea or Lee. 7, Mimram. 8, Beane. 9, Rib. 10, Quin. 11, Ash 12, Stort. 13, Purwell. 14,Oughton. 15, Hiz. 16, Ivel. 17, Rhee. 18, Thame.

30) HERTFORDSHIRE IN LITERATURE

1, The Compleat Angler - Izaak Walton. 2, Charles Lamb. 3, John Gilpin - William Cowper. 4, Queen Hoo Hall. 5, Twelfth Night. 6, Rupert Brooke. 7, Pride and Prejudice - Jane Austen. 8, Sir John Betjeman. 9, Rupert Brooke. 10, Edward Lear.

31) NATURAL HISTORY

1, Marsworth Reservoir at Tring. 2, It is one of the very few in Britain where most of the nests are in reed beds, and not in trees. 3. The existence in pure, clear, cold water of two species of flat worms - *Crenobia alpina* and *Polycelis felina*, which have existed since the Ice Age. 4, Hooded Crow, (also known in England as the Grey Crow or Royston Crow). 5, Panshanger Park (a private park). 6, Black-necked Grebe. 7, Hornbeam. 8, Ashridge Estate. 9, Dotterel. 10, Great Bustard.

32) MORE VILLAGE PUBLIC HOUSES

1, F. 2, D. 3, G. 4, A. 5, J. 6, H. 7, B. 8, C. 9, E. 10, I.

33) TOWN TWINNING

1, F. 2, G. 3, H. 4, A., 5, J. 6, I. 7, B. 8, C. 9, E. 10, D.

34) GENERAL

1, Bishop's Palace, Much Hadham. 2, Long Marston. 3, Croxley Green. 4, Brent Pelham - Aldbury. 5, Tring. 6, TRUST AND FEAR NOT. 7, Tring Park. 8, Health Farm. 9, Salisbury Hall near London Colney. 10, At the premises of Concrete Utilities, Great Amwell.

35) BREWERIES

1, F. 2, G. 3, I. 4, H. 5, C. 6, A. 7, J. 8, B. 9, E. 10, D.

36) MORE VILLAGE PUBLIC HOUSES

1, D. 2, F. 3, J. 4, H. 5, B. 6, A. 7, I. 8, C. 9, G. 10, E.

37) PEOPLE - FAMOUS, NOTEWORTHY OR INFAMOUS

1, Sir Henry Wood. 2, Sir Arthur Sullivan. 3, William Penn. 4, John Loudon McAdam. 5, Richard Cromwell. 6, Richard Rumbold. 7, Sir Hugh Middleton. 8, By poaching. They were convicted of offences against the Game Laws (Poaching). 9, Lucas came from a wealthy family of landowners, and lived at Elmwood House with his widowed mother. When she died in 1849 he kept the body in the house for three months until Police and Clergy broke in and took it for burial. He then barricaded himself in the house by nailing heavy timbers across doors and windows. He wore no clothes but just wrapped himself in a blanket, and lived thus for twenty-five years. He spoke to tramps and some visitors through iron bars on the kitchen window. He lived in complete squalor until it was thought that he was ill, and in 1874 Police accompanied by Doctors broke into the house and took him to hospital, where he died shortly afterwards. He had become well known as 'The Hermit of Redcoats,' and was on one occasion visited by Charles Dickens, who wrote about him in an essay. It is also thought that Dickens's character Mr. Mopes in Tom Tiddler's Ground is based on Lucas. There is a public house named after him. 10, He was a footpad, and was robbing a local farmer, when he was shot and killed by a friend of the farmer.

38) HAILEYBURY SCHOOL

1, Hertford Heath. 2, 1809. 3, Civil Servants of the East India Company. 4, 1862. 5, William Wilkins. 6, Sir John Lawrence 1811-1879. 7. Lord Allenby 1861-1936. 8, 577. 9. They all won the Victoria Cross during the First World War. 10, Clement Atlee.

39) CHURCHES

1, St. Mary Magdelene, Flaunden. 2, St. Margaret. Ridge. 3. St. John the Baptist, Cottered. 4. Hunsdon. 5, St. Mary. Essendon. 6, St. Mary the Virgin, Braughing - 1562. 7. Buntingford - St. Richard of Chichester. 8, Much Hadham. 9. New St. Lawrence, Ayot St. Lawrence. 10. The altar is at the west end of the church.

40) GENERAL

1. Ashwell. 2, Just over 400 years ago a local farmer, Matthew Wall, a widower fell ill, and was thought to have died. On 2nd October, as his coffin was being carried to the church for burial, one of the pall bearers slipped on wet leaves, and the coffin fell to the ground. Noises were heard inside the coffin, it was opened up and Wall sat up. He recovered from the shock, and his illness and later married again and raised a family, and died in 1595. In his will he left a shilling for the leaves to be swept from the lane where his coffin was dropped, and a shilling for the tolling of the funeral bell. Children from the local school still

sweep the leaves every year and the funeral bell is tolled. More bells are rung later in the day to commemorate his wedding. 3, 1938 - Waltham Cross. 4, Trolley Buses until 1960. 5, Great Munden. 6. Maran. 7. Chiltern Langley. 8. Abbots Walden. 9. Chipperfield. 10. A Boarding School for girls.

41) INDUSTRIES - PAST AND PRESENT

1, Paper. 2, Silk. 3. Ware - during the 18th century over 1000 tons of malt were sent by barge from Ware to London every week, and in the 19th century there were at one time 70 maltings in Ware. 4. Film making. 5, Straw Plaiting, for the straw hat making industry in nearby Luton. 6, Making bearskin hats for the Grenadier Guards. It is the only place that they are made. 7, Market gardening and nurseries, with acres and acres under glass, growing tomatoes, cucumbers, roses, carnations and chrysanthemums as main crops. 8, Wilfred Harkness - rose growing. 9, Silk worm farming. 10, Race horse training.

42) MORE VILLAGE PUBLIC HOUSES

1, D. 2, I. 3, H. 4, G. 5, J. 6, A. 7, F. 8, B. 9, C. 10, E.

43) MORE NOTEWORTIIY HERTFORDIANS

1, Baron John Somers of Evesham. 2, John Eliot. 3, Charles Chauncey. 4, Lord Anson. 5, A,J. Balfour. 6, Alfred and Sir Otto Beit. 7, Sir Richard Whittington.

8, King Michael of Rumania. 9. Bishops Stortford. 10, Count Esterhazy - villain of the Dreyfus case.

44) MORE TOWN TWINNING

1, E. 2, F. 3, G. 4, H. 5, C. 6, J. 7, I. 8, B. 9, A. 10, D.

45) GENERAL

1, 631 square miles. 2, Hastoe Hill, south of Tring (244 metres). 3, West Hyde. 4, Hinxworth. 5, Puttenham. 6, Lea or Lee. 7, Grounds at Ashridge (but not the house), and Shaw's Corner, Ayot St. Lawrence. 8, Munden Furnival and Much Munden. 9, The Gatehouse, at Rye House, Hoddesdon. 10, The gateway of the former St. Albans prison.

46) ODD ONE OUT

1, Haldens, which is in Welwyn Garden City. The others are in Stevenage. 2, Icknield. The Icknield Way is pre-Roman, the others are Roman roads. 3, Hormead. The only one, which is not a Pelham. 4, Garston, which is in Watford, the others are in Hemel Hampstead. 5, Ravensburgh Castle, which was an Iron Age fort, the others are Norman Castles. 6, Uttlesford, which is in Essex, the others are districts in Hertfordshire. 7, Hartham, which is in Hertford, the others are in Welwyn Garden City. 8, Stockers, which is a lake in the Colne Valley, the others are reservoirs at Tring. 9, Oxlease, which is in Hatfield, the others are in St. Albans. 10, The Gade, which is a River flowing into the Colne, the others are rivers running into the Lea or Lee.

47) GENERAL

1, Theobald's Park, Cheshunt. 2, Letchmore Heath. 3, The George and Dragon at Codicote. 4, Jonas Fosbrooke. 5, 1931 at Rye House, Hoddesdon. 6, The Victoria and Albert Museum. 7, Gazebos. 8, Thomas Hobson, Hobson's choice. 9, Piers Shonks. 10, Walkern.

48) PUBLIC HOUSES NAMED AFTER PEOPLE

1, F. 2, I. 3, H. 4, J. 5, G. 6, A. 7, B. 8, C. 9, D. 10, E.

49) GENERAL
1, Burnham Green. 2, Datchworth. 3, Henry Trigg. 4, Sawbridgeworth. 5, Weston. 6, July 1800, on the Old North Road (now the A10) between Puckeridge and Westmill. He was shot by Colonel Manners whilst attempting to rob him of the wages he was carrying to soldiers at Cambridge. The identity of the highwayman was never discovered, and he was buried in Westmill churchyard. 7, Boxmoor Common. 8, Nudist colonies - there were eight there at one time. 9, Baghdad - formerly known as Baldach, a city occupied by the Knights Templar. 10, Buntingford.

50) CHURCHES

1, Bishops Stortford. 2, Instead of the 'Hertfordshire Spike' (see page 72), they have four pinnacles on the tower; Royston on the tower which was added in the late 16th century, Northaw and Bovington on the original 19th century churches and Barkway, when the tower was rebuilt in 1861. 3, They are all Redundant Churches looked after by The Churches Conservation Trust. 4, The half-circular apse. Some later churches have had them added but they are not Norman. 5, Widford. 6, St. Michael, St. Albans. 7, Little Hadham. 8, St. Mary Magdalene, Barkway. 9, St. Mary Magdalene, Caldicote. 10, St. Edmund of Canterbury, Old Hall Green near Puckeridge. It is the chapel built for St. Edmunds College in 1853.

51) THOROUGHFARES

1, Hitchin. 2, Welwyn Garden City. 3, Bishops Stortford. 4, Potters Bar. 5, Stevenage. 6, Hertford. 7, Watford. 8, Hemel Hempstead. 9, Letchworth. 10, Borehamwood.

52) CHURCHES

1, Hemel Hempstead. 2, Hertford. 3, All Saints Pastoral Centre - a Catholic Retreat. 4, St. Mary and St. Thomas, Knebworth. 5, Holy Trinity, Throcking. 147 metres. 6. They do not have towers, but small bell-cotes. 7, St. Mary the Virgin, Furneux Pelham. 8,

St. Mary, Puttenham. 9, Wheathampstead. 10, Baldock.

53) GENERAL

1, The Eight Bells, 2, Hawkshead Road, between Potters Bar and Brookmans Park. 3, Little Berkhamsted. 4, Scotts Road, Ware. 5, Mackery End. 6, From the name of the 12th century Danius Hundred (Danius for Danes and Hundred an early administrative division of a county). Later the Latin version Danicorum was used and this was eventually shortened to Dacorum. 7, Chorleywood, founded in March 1890. (Two others, West Herts and Boxmoor, were founded later the same year.) 8, Sarratt. 9, Lady Rosia, wife of a Norman noble of Newsells Manor erected a cross where Ermine Street crossed the Icknield Way. It was known as Rosia's Cross; it later became Rosia's Town and then Royston. 10, Hinxworth.

54) CHURCHES

1, St. Mary, Hertingfordbury. 2, They all have broach spires; that is a spire that runs up from the walls of the tower, or even juts out over the walls, and does not have a parapet around it. 3, Mass Dials - primitive forms of sun dials, found on some medieval churches. They consist of a few lines scratched into the stonework, and a gnomon, which showed the time for Mass. 4, St. Michael and All Angels, Watford. 5, St. Mary the Virgin, Ashwell. 6, High Wych. 7, St.

James, Stanstead Abbots. 8, Ickleford. 9, Hatfield. 10, St. Mary, Pirton.

55) PUBLIC HOUSES WITH ANIMAL NAMES

1, E. 2, A. 3, I. 4, H. 5, B. 6, G. 7, C. 8, J. 9, D. 10, F.

56) MORE TOWN (AND VILLAGE) TWINNING

1, E. 2, I. 3, H. 4, G. 5, B. 6, J. 7, A. 8, F. 9. C. 10, D.

57) GENERAL

1, 1903. 2, 1919. 3, Anstey. 4, Great Munden. 5, Kings Langley. 6, Ardeley. 7, Brickendon Liberty. 8, Barkway. 9, Along the Grand Union Canal. 10, Batford.

58) TOWNS AND VILLAGES BEGINNING WITH THE LETTER B

1, Berkhamsted. 2,Bovingdon. 3, Boxmoor. 4, Bushey. 5, Bricket Wood. 6, Borehamwood. 7, Bentley Heath. 8, Brookmans Park. 9, Broxbourne. 10, Bayford. 11, Brickendon. 12, Bramfield. 13, Benington. 14, Baldock. 15, Bygrave. 16, Barley. 17, Barkway. 18, Buckland. 19, Brent Pelham. 20, Buntingford. 21, Braughing. 22, Bishops Stortford.

59) VILLAGES BEGINNING WITH A VOWEL

1, Aldbury. 2, East Hyde. 3, Offley. 4, Ickleford. 5, Ippollitts. 6, Ashwell. 7, Ayot St. Lawrence. 8, Ayot St. Peter. 9, Aston. 10, Ardeley. 11, Aspenden. 12, Anstey. 13, Albury. 14, Oxhey. 15, Abbots Langley. 16, Aldenham. 17, Elstree. 18, Essendon. 19 Epping Green. 20, Eastwick.

60) PUBLIC HOUSES WITH BIRD NAMES

1, C. 2, I. 3, A. 4, H. 5, G. 6, J. 7, E. 8, D. 9, F. 10, B.